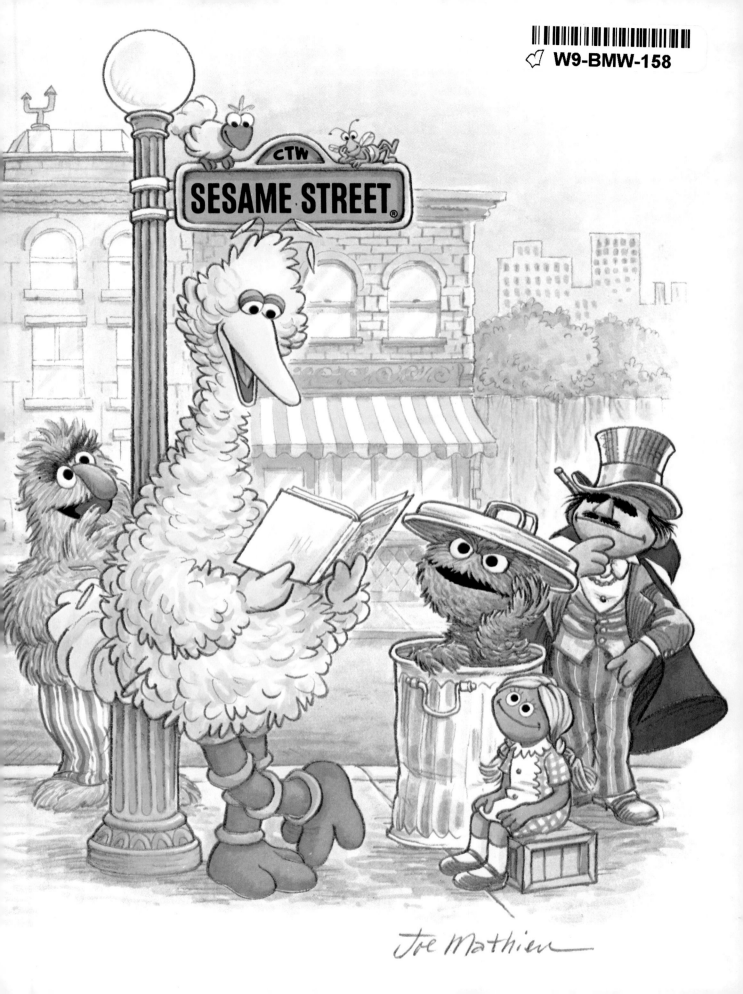

THE SESAME STREET® LIBRARY

With Jim Henson's Muppets

VOLUME 14

FEATURING THE NUMBER 14

Children's Television Workshop/Funk & Wagnalls, Inc.

WRITTEN BY:
Emily Perl Kingsley
Patricia Thackray

ILLUSTRATED BY:
Art-so-fine
A. Delaney
Lawrence Di Fiori
Joseph Mathieu
Marc Nadel
Mary Schenck
Kay Wood

PHOTOGRAPHS BY:
Bonnie Erickson
Wayde Harrison
Neil Selkirk

THE COUNT AT THE TWIDDLEBUG PICNIC
Featuring the Number 14

One sunny April fourteenth, fourteen Twiddlebugs decided to have a picnic. They planned it perfectly—there were fourteen of everything!

Just as they had everything set out for their picnic, along came the Count. "Springtime is wonderful," said the Count, "there is so much to count!"

Suddenly, he spied a tiny tablecloth in the grass. Bending over, he saw fourteen tiny Twiddlebugs having a picnic.

"Wonderful, wonderful!" said the Count. "What a wonderful day for a picnic!"

"Yes," said the Twiddlebugs, "if it doesn't rain, like last year."

"Rain!" said the Count. "Impossible! I could not find a single cloud in the sky to count. Do you mind if I join you?"

"Certainly not," they replied. "But we only have enough for fourteen."

"Fourteen!" cried the Count. "My favorite number! I do not wish to disturb you, I only want to lie here and count. Carry on, carry on with your wonderful picnic."

"Suit yourself," they said.

KEERAKK!

The Twiddlebugs began to pass around their fourteen jelly sandwiches.

"Aha!" said the Count. "One little jelly sandwich! Two little jelly sandwiches!! Three little jelly sandwiches!!!"

There was a flash of lightning and the sound of thunder as the Count counted the sandwiches. The Twiddlebugs looked up nervously.

"You don't think it will rain, do you?" they asked.

"It is nothing," said the Count. "Do not worry! Eat, little Twiddlebugs, eat! Eight cups of Twiddle punch. Nine cups of Twiddle punch!!....."

The Count counted everything on the Twiddlebug menu, while they worried more and more about the rain.

"Twelve adorable little cupcakes! Thirteen adorable little cupcakes!!" said the Count. "This is so *exciting*! FOURTEEN adorable little cupcakes!!!"

Thunder and lightning crashed around the tiny picnic and the Count kept counting.

The Twiddlebugs were starting to pack up and run home, when one of them cried, "Wait! Wait! We don't have to go home!" And she handed out fourteen little red-and-white-polka-dot umbrellas.

"Look at that!" cried the Count. "I thought that I had counted everything. First I will count the umbrellas, and then I will count the polka dots! One little red-and-white-polka-dot umbrella! Two little red-and-white-polka-dot umbrellas!! *Three* little red-and-white-polka-dot umbrellas!!! Wonderful, wonderful. A wonderful picnic!"

And it was!

Which picture of Grover is different?

Which picture of Ernie is different?

Which picture of Cookie Monster is different?

What is a magnifying glass?

What is a **magnifying glass**?
A **magnifying glass** is a special tool.
A **magnifying glass** makes things look bigger.
When you make something look bigger, you are **magnifying it**.
How do you use a **magnifying glass**?
You hold it up to your eye, and look through the glass part.
You look at whatever you want to see bigger.
What do things look like through a **magnifying glass**?
Look at the next page.

Here is a picture of a **magnifying glass**.

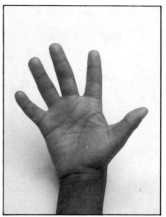

Here is a picture of somebody's hand.

Here is a picture of the same hand through a **magnifying glass**.

Here is a picture of some stamps.

Here is a picture of the same stamps through a **magnifying glass**.

You can make your own **magnifying glass**!
Here's what you do:
Get a plain glass.
Fill it half-full of water.
Put the glass on a table.
Sit at the table so your nose is right on the edge.
Put your hand behind the glass.
Does your hand look bigger?

What other things can you look at through your **magnifying glass**?

Larry Di Fiori
Photographs by Neil Selkirk

In and Out

Grover is **IN** the bathtub.

Grover is **OUT** of the bathtub.

Grover is **IN** the airplane.

Grover is **OUT** of the airplane.

Grover is **IN** the barrel.

Grover is **OUT** of the barrel.

Is Grover **IN** or **OUT**?

Is Grover **IN** or **OUT**?

Is Grover **IN** or **OUT**?

Is Grover **IN** or **OUT**?

Three Monster Catch

Grover and Cookie Monster were playing catch. Herry Monster walked over to Grover and Cookie. "Can I play ball with you?" Herry Monster asked.

"Oh, that is a good idea," Grover said. "We will play Three Monster Catch. We will stand in a circle and throw the ball to each other. First I throw the ball to Cookie. Then Cookie throws the ball to Herry. Then Herry throws the ball to me. Won't that be fun? First, I Grover, will throw the ball to Cookie Monster." Grover threw the ball to Cookie. Cookie Monster caught the ball.

"Next, me, Cookie Monster, will eat the ball," said Cookie.

"No! No!" said Grover. "Don't eat the ball! Throw it to Herry Monster."

"Yes, me know," said Cookie. "Me only kidding." So Cookie Monster threw the ball to Herry. But Herry did not put his hands out to catch it. The ball landed on the ground.

"Stop the game!" said Grover. "What is the matter, Herry? You forgot to catch the ball."

Herry looked very sad. "I didn't forget, Grover," said Herry. "I . . . . I don't know how to catch a ball." And Herry started to cry.

"Don't cry, Herry," said Grover. "Cookie and I will teach you how to catch."

"You will?" sobbed Herry. "Gee, that's great."

Grover and Cookie showed Herry how to hold his hands together in front of his body to catch the ball. Then Cookie threw Herry the ball. But the ball bounced right out of Herry's hands.

"Herry, my good friend," Grover said, "You have to hold the ball tightly when it lands in your hands. Try again." So Herry tried again. Grover threw him the ball. This time it bounced off Herry's chest.

"Look at ball, Herry," Cookie explained, "don't look at your hands. You see ball coming, then move hands to catch it."

"Oh, I'll never learn how to catch!" said Herry. "I'm going home. You two play without me."

"Hold it Her--ry!" said Grover. "Do not give up. I had to practice two weeks before I could catch a ball. Now, try again."

Catch it!

So Cookie and Grover kept throwing the ball to Herry. Soon, he was able to catch it.

"Now," Grover said, "we can all catch, so let us play Three Monster Catch."

Just as they were about to start playing, Big Bird came along. "Hi, everybody!" he said. "Can I play, too?"

"Sure," said Herry. "Here, catch the ball." And he threw the ball to Big Bird.

"But I don't know how to catch," said Big Bird.

"You don't ?" said Herry. "Well, Big Bird, take it from me—all you need is a little practice. I will teach you how to catch the ball."

So Herry Monster taught Big Bird how to catch the ball, and they all played Three Monster and One Bird Catch until it was time to go home.

Catch the ball Herry!

DiFiori

Toni Delaney

In the Size of the Beholder

One warm, spring day, Big Bird decided to take a walk. He put his good luck penny in his hand and started off. As soon as he left his nest, Big Bird banged his head on a tree branch. "Ouch!" he yelled. "I'm so big! I'm always banging my head."

A few minutes later, Big Bird tripped over a rock and fell down. "Ouch!" he yelled again. "I'm so big and tall that I didn't even see that rock way down there on the ground," Big Bird said. "I hate being such a big bird. I'm always getting in the way and bumping into things. My head is up so high that I trip over things because I can't see them. I wish I were little."

Just then, Little Bird swooped down in front of Big Bird. He had a balloon in his beak and was all out of breath.

"Hello, Little Bird," said Big Bird. "Where did you come from?"

"I've been flying after this balloon," said Little Bird. "I got so tired that I just had to rest. I'm too little. I have to flap my wings so hard to get anywhere fast. I hate being little. Everyone I know is big. I have to try really hard to keep up with my friends. Sometimes they even forget I'm there because I'm so little."

"Gee," said Big Bird. "I didn't know that being little was hard. I just thought it was hard being big."

"Well, I thought being big was the most wonderful thing in the world," said Little Bird.

While Little Bird and Big Bird were thinking about being little and big, Little Bird's balloon escaped and started to float away.

"You can get that balloon, Big Bird!" said Little Bird. "You have long legs and can take big steps."

Big Bird caught up with the balloon in no time and gave it back to Little Bird. "Being big can be very helpful," said Big Bird happily.

Just then, Big Bird's lucky penny dropped from his hand and rolled under the step. "Oh no! My good luck penny! I'm too big to fit under that step to get it!"

"But I'm not!" said Little Bird. And he marched proudly over to the step, stuck his beak underneath and pulled out the penny. "Being little isn't so bad after all," said Little Bird.

So, Big Bird and Little Bird walked down Sesame Street together. Big Bird was happy to be big. And Little Bird was very happy to be little.

Red Light, Green Light

You and your friends are going to the park to play in the snow. Who will get there first?

1. Take a penny and trace two circles on a piece of white paper. Color one circle red and the other circle green. Cut out the circles and tape one circle on each side of the penny.
2. Each person playing should use a different playing piece. You can use coins or buttons.

Now you are ready to play.

1. Put your playing pieces on the start arrow.
2. Flip the penny. If you get the green side, GO. Move your playing piece one space. Then flip the penny again. You can keep moving as long as you get the green side of the penny.
3. When you get the red side, STOP and pass the penny on.
4. Whose turn is next? Give the penny to that player.
5. Who gets to the park first?

SESAME STREE

START

FINISH

Mary Schenck

Grover's Bedtime Story

"Thank you very much for inviting me to sleep over at your house, Grover," said Prairie Dawn. "I've had such a good time."

"Oh, it is fun to have somebody come to visit and sleep over," said Grover. "I am glad you could come. But now it is late and I think we had better go to sleep."

"Uh, Grover?" said Prairie Dawn.

"There is just one little thing. I like to hear a bedtime story before I go to sleep. When I am home, my daddy usually tells me a story."

"Hmm. That is a problem," said Grover. "We could call your daddy on the telephone and he could tell you a story over the phone. How would that be?"

"I have a better idea," said Prairie

Dawn. "Why don't *you* tell me a bedtime story?"

"Me?" said Grover. "*Me??* Cute, furry, adorable old Grover? Tell you a bedtime story?"

"Why not?" said Prairie Dawn. "I am sure you know lots of nice stories."

"Er, well," said Grover, "I have not told many bedtime stories before. In fact, *none* is how many bedtime

stories I have told. None at all. I really do not know how to tell a bedtime story."

"Oh, I am sure you can do it," said Prairie Dawn. "You just start at the beginning and the rest will take care of itself." She got into bed and pulled the covers up around her chin. "O.K., Grover, I am ready. You can start your bedtime story now."

"Oh, dear," said Grover. "How to do this. . . . Just start at the beginning and see what happens, huh? Ahem. All right. . . .

"Once upon a time . . . " he began. "Yes, that is an excellent *beginning* to my story. Once upon a time! Once upon a time. Once upon a time."

"Uh, Grover," said Prairie Dawn, "what comes next?"

"I beg your pardon?" asked Grover.

"Well," said Prairie Dawn, "all you said was 'Once upon a time.' There has to be more to the story than that! That is just a *beginning* to the story. What happens next?"

"Ohhhh," said Grover. "You want to know what happens next! Of course you do! Heh, heh. Um . . . well . . . let me see. . . .

"Once upon a time," Grover began again, ". . . um . . . well . . . they lived happily ever after! There you are!"

"Grover!" said Prairie Dawn. "What kind of story is that? That is not the way to tell a story! Once upon a time they lived happily ever after? That is ridiculous!"

"You did not like the way it ended?" asked Grover. "I always thought 'they lived happily ever after' was a very nice ending to a story."

"The beginning was O.K., and the ending was O.K. . . . but there was no middle."

"No middle?" said Grover. "What is a *middle*?"

"The middle is the *story* part of the story—where everything happens!" explained Prairie Dawn. "You left out the whole middle part!"

"I am sorry, Prairie Dawn," said Grover. "I told you I did not have much experience in telling bedtime stories."

"Well, let me show you how it works," said Prairie Dawn. Then you will know how, and you can tell me *my* bedtime story."

"That is an excellent idea!" said Grover.

"O.K.," said Prairie Dawn. "First you start your story with 'Once upon a time,' just as you did. But then you follow it with the middle part of the story. So here goes:

"Once upon a time there was a king named Roundtree and he had a very smart and beautiful daughter named Victoria Joyce. One day a wicked magician came and put a spell on the three good fairies who were weaving an enchanted cloak in which to wrap the mysterious silver apple so that it could be delivered to the wondrous wizard of the West, so their fingers turned into string beans and they could no longer weave the enchanted cloak. But the brave little girl mesmerized the six fire-breathing dragons that guarded the castle gate and flew on the magic flying horse, Basingstoke, through the skies, dodging the evil eagles and horrid hawks that swooped and darted at her, on to the wizard's palace, where she delivered the silver apple to the wizard all by herself. The wizard was so amazed at Victoria's splendid feats of bravery and courage that he presented her with a beautiful singing bird and a flower that would always be in bloom. The evil witches on the mountains gnashed their

teeth and pulled out their hair because they had wanted the singing bird and the amazing ever-blooming flower but they knew they could not fight against such a glorious girl as Victoria Joyce and Victoria sailed home to her father's castle on the back of a great golden swan . . . and . . . and here is where you put the ending part on, Grover, and . . . she lived happily ever after!

There. You see how easy it is to tell a bedtime story? But you absolutely must have the middle part or else it is not a story at all. Do you understand now, Grover? . . . Grover? . . . Grover??"

But Grover had fallen fast asleep.

"Oh dear," said Prairie Dawn. "Now I've *done* it. I told such a good story that I put Grover to sleep. Now what am I going to do? I'll be up all night."

Just then the door opened and Grover's mommy came into the room.

"Would you like to hear a bedtime story, Prairie Dawn?" asked Grover's mommy. "I used to tell bedtime stories to Grover but he would always fall asleep right after the 'Once upon a time' part. He never heard the middle and the end. It would be a great treat for me to be able to tell a bedtime story to someone who could stay awake long enough to hear the 'happily ever after' part."

"Oh, thank you," said Prairie Dawn. And she curled up under the covers as Grover's mommy sat down beside the bed.

"Once upon a time . . ." began Grover's mommy. . . .

Bert lost **14** pigeons.
Can you help him find them?

Food for Thought

Can you name the food that
you see on this page?
Touch a carrot.
Touch an apple.
What else do you see?

Turn the page.

What food do you see on this page?
Find a carrot.
Find a mushroom.

Three people are just about to eat lunch.
Who do you think they are?
Turn the page.

You are what you eat!

Look closely.

What is Bert made of?

What is Ernie made of?

What is the Junk Food Monster made of?

Why do we exercise?

Exercise is fun. It makes us feel good.
Exercise keeps our bodies strong and stretchy.
The more we exercise, the longer we are able to play without getting tired.
Some exercises are not easy to do when we first learn them.
But if we keep trying and do not give up,
we will be able to do our exercises better and better.
Some people like to do yoga exercises.
Some people like to do dance exercises.
Some people like to do stretching exercises.
What kind of exercises do you like to do?
Do you like to play sports?
Did you know that exercise helps us to play sports better?
Exercise helps us to do everything better!

J. Mathieu

Big Bird's Banana Bread

Let's make banana bread!
It's better than
a birdseed sundae!
It's easy.
Just follow the directions.

Here is what you will need:
3 peeled ripe bananas
3/4 cup honey
1/4 cup melted butter
1/2 teaspoon baking soda
1 1/2 cups whole wheat flour
1 big bowl
1 big wooden spoon
1 fork
1 bread pan (rub some cooking
oil around the inside of it)
1 wire cooling rack
1 measuring cup
1 set of measuring spoons

Here's what you need a grownup to do:
1. Turn the oven on to 350 degrees.
2. Melt 1/4 cup of butter in a pan.
I asked Mr. Looper to help me.
He was happy to help!

Here's what you do:

1 Put the peeled bananas in a bowl.

2 Mash up the bananas with the back of a fork.

3 Add the melted butter.

4 Add:
1/2 teaspoon baking soda
1 1/2 cups whole wheat flour
3/4 cup honey

5 Stir everything in the bowl with the big spoon. Stir until everything is mixed together.

6 Pour the mix into the oiled bread pan.

7 Bake for one hour.

8 After one hour, put a toothpick in the bread.
Is there some bread on the toothpick when you pull it out?
If there is, let the bread cook for a little while longer.
If there is no bread on the toothpick when you pull it out,
the bread is done!

9 Ask your grown-up helper to take the bread out of the oven.
They need to take the bread out of the pan,
and put it on the wire rack.

10 When the bread is cool,
cut it up and share
it with your neighbors!

Look again! What do you see on this page now?

Now you're at the top of the building, looking down!

What do you see on this page?

You're standing at the bottom of this building, looking up.
Turn the book upside down.

THE MONSTERS' ALPHABET

C Cookie

D Door

E Elephant

F Fire Truck

G Goose

H House

I Ice Cream

J Jump Rope

K Kangaroo

L Lion

M Moon

N Net

O Octopus

P Paint

Q Queen

R Rainbow

S Sandwich

T Telephone

U Umbrella

V Valentine

W Wishing Well

X X-ray

Y Yo-Yo

Z Zipper

The end!